Text copyright © 2002 Evelyn Bence.
Artwork by Cassandre Maxwell © 2002.
ISBN# 0-88271-301-9

The Saint Who Became
Santa Claus

Written by
Evelyn Bence

Illustrated by
Cassandre Maxwell

Regina Press
New York

On Christmas Eve, after everyone is in bed and asleep, Santa Claus visits children's homes everywhere. He carries a sack full of presents on his back, leaves his gifts and is gone before we hear a door slam or the sleigh bells ring as he rides away. On Christmas morning we shout, "Santa Claus was here! Thank you, Santa Claus!" But he doesn't want us to thank him. He wants us to give thanks to the Christ child, Jesus, whose birthday we celebrate. We call him Santa Claus and this is his story....

It happened long ago in a country we now call Turkey, in the town of Myra by the sea. A rich Christian father and mother had a baby boy. They named him Nicholas, which means "Champion of the People."

Nicholas grew to be a fine young man. When his parents died, he inherited a lot of money. Nicholas started giving gifts to the people of Myra. He made sure to help those less fortunate than himself, especially the family with three daughters.

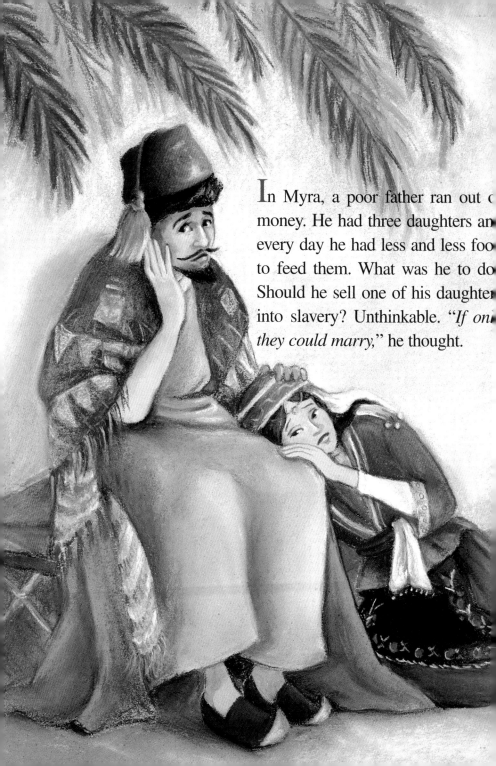

In Myra, a poor father ran out of money. He had three daughters and every day he had less and less food to feed them. What was he to do? Should he sell one of his daughters into slavery? Unthinkable. "*If only they could marry,*" he thought.

In Myra, a girl couldn't marry unless her family gave her husband a gift of gold. This was to help the new family buy a house, or a bed or a table. Unfortunately, the father had no gold to give.

Nicholas heard the man was in trouble and that his daughters were in danger. He counted out some gold coins, wrapped them in a round sack, threw it over his back and walked out into the street. Even though it was very dark, he found the house, reached through an open window and dropped the sack onto the floor.

In the morning, the family found the gold, but they didn't
know who had left it there, so they simply thanked God for
their gift! First, their father bought some food. Then he gave
some gold to a fine young man who married his first daughter
and bought her a new house by the sea. Soon the father ran out
of money. As a result, he thought of selling his second
daughter into slavery!

Nicholas found out about the father's problem. Again, he wrapped some gold coins into a sack and went out into the dark night. He snuck up to the same window, dropped the sack and ran away.

In the morning when the girls found the gold, they didn't know who gave it to them so they simply thanked God for their gift. Then their father gave some gold to a fine young man who married his second daughter and bought a table for their new house on the road out of town.

Now, the father had one daughter living at home with him, but he would soon run out of money.

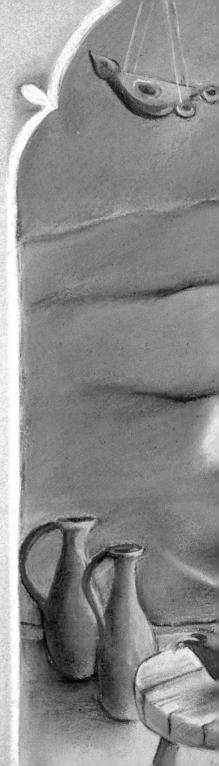

Upon hearing this, Nicholas packed a third bag of gold, and made another secret trip across town. This time the father heard the noise and ran to the door.

"Hey, Nicholas!" he shouted. Nicholas was discovered.

"Don't tell anyone that I gave you the gold." Nicholas said. "Let it be our secret. And don't thank me. Thank God."

But it was hard to keep the secret. Soon, everyone in Myra knew.

Nicholas became known all over Myra as "Champion of the People", and the church made him the Bishop of Myra. He grew a beard and rode through town on a horse, wearing his red bishop's robe. Nicholas taught people about the love of Jesus and how people can love one another by helping each other and doing good deeds.

One year, there was such bad weather in Myra that farmers couldn't grow grain for cereal and bread. Hungry children asked Bishop Nicholas to help them. Nicholas prayed and God heard his prayer. A ship full of grain was sailing far out to sea. That night, the captain had a dream. In his dream a man with a beard handed him three pieces of gold and said, *Take your ship to Myra.* When the captain woke he had three pieces of gold in his hand! "Turn the ship to Myra!" shouted the captain to his crew. Upon hearing his instructions, they did as they were told.

When the ship sailed into port, Bishop Nicholas greeted it. The captain blinked his eyes. "What!?" Nicholas looked just like the man in the captain's dream. He was the mysterious night visitor who put the gold in the captain's hand!

The captain sold all his grain to Nicholas. Everyone thanked God for this wonderful gift. Then they made some delicious bread and the children were hungry no more.

Nicholas lived for many years, serving the people of Myra. After he died the church named him a Saint — Saint Nicholas. "The Champion of the People" became known as the "Saint Who Loves Children."

Some people called him Saint Nick. In Holland, they called him Sinter (for Saint) and Claes (for Nicholas) — Sinter Claes! Soon his name was changed to Santa Claus!

Near his feast day on December 6th, children all around the world began to ask him for special gifts. Some children began to ask him to bring presents to those less fortunate than themselves.

Now, every Christmas, children around the world wait for Saint Nicholas to visit their homes, secretly, at night. When they find gifts under their Christmas tree, they shout, "Santa Claus was here! Thank you, Santa Claus!"

But he doesn't want to be thanked. He only wants to show us how important it is to share what we have with others, and to thank God for all the gifts we receive.

Most of all, Saint Nicholas wants us to thank God for the gift of the Christ Child, Jesus, who taught us how to love one another; and whose birth makes Christmas a Holy Day for all of us.